D0420163

Everyday Maths

Everyday Maths

A refresher course for adults

JOHN GOLDSMITH

SERENDIPITY

First published in 2002 by
Serendipity
Suite 530
37 Store Street
Bloomsbury
London

British Library cataloguing in publication data
A catalogue record for this book is available from the British Library

ISBN 1–84394–028–0

Printed and bound by
Biddles Ltd, Guildford

Contents

Introduction

The cricket commentator is summing-up at the end of the day's play – 'England finish the day on 186 for 7 wickets, the target to avoid the follow on is 250 so they require another ——', at this point the summary breaks down since the speaker cannot perform a simple subtraction. 'Maths was never my best subject at school', is the excuse given.

This implies that our basic arithmetic has become rusty. For this state of affairs calculators must take some of the blame. In a recent article in the *Daily Telegraph*, John Casey, a Cambridge Don, suggests that 'something will have gone wrong if a whole generation of children are helpless without pocket calculators. There must sometimes be occasions when you need to add up in your head or on a piece of paper. But the deeper worry is whether a total reliance on calculators means that you do not understand what numerical calculation is'. Like other skills, such as First Aid and Life Saving, Mathematics requires constant application to keep it in good working order.

This manual is a refresher course for adults who have lost touch with the subject. It deals first with whole numbers – the 'grammar' of mathematics – and the four basic operations of arithmetic – addition, multiplication, subtraction and division. This is followed by fractions, percentages and degrees and other branches of mathematics – geometry, algebra and trigonometry.

Practical applications of the subject matter are included throughout the book. Solutions and answers to questions can be found at the back of the book. Exercises, to keep your mental arithmetic fresh, such as supermarket shopping to a budget and checking monthly bank statements, are also discussed.

Whole numbers

In the English language, the letters of the alphabet – A, B, C, D, E, F, G, H, I, J, K, L, M, N, O, P, Q, R, S, T, U, V, W, X, Y, Z – are the 'building blocks' from which words are formed. These, in turn, are used to make sentences.

Similarly, in mathematics, the 'building blocks' are numbers – 1, 2, 3, 4, 5, 6, 7, 8, 9, 10, etc. – which represent quantities. An important difference is that, whereas the alphabet contains a fixed number of letters (26), numbers are infinite, running into millions, billions, trillions, and zillions.

What can we do with numbers? Firstly, we can perform the following operations.

Operation	Mathematical symbol
Addition	+
Multiplication	×
Subtraction	−
Division	÷

Addition

Addition is the adding together of quantities to form a greater one.

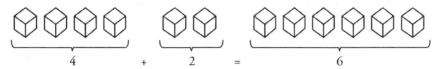

Here are some quick tips:
  To add 9: add 10 and subtract 1
  To add 8: add 10 and subtract 2

When adding a series of numbers, scan them for combinations of digits which add up to 10 or multiples of 10. For example:
  To add 7, 14 and 23:

  $7 + 23 = 30$, add $14 = 44$.

  To add 35, 8, 16, 45 and 12:

  $35 + 45 = 80$, $8 + 12 = 20$, $80 + 20 = 100$, add $16 = 116$.

The traditional way to add numbers is to set them out in vertical columns. Thus:

8765, 432, 91 and 8	8765
The total in the right hand column is 16,	432
the '1' in the 16 being carried over to the	91
next column; this procedure is repeated for	8
the final two columns.	9296

An alternative method is to add the thousands, hundreds, tens and digits separately. Thus in the above example:

$$8000 = 8000$$
$$700 + 400 = 1100$$
$$60 + 30 + 90 = 180$$
$$5 + 2 + 1 + 8 = 16$$
$$9296$$

Addition questions

I would suggest that the questions are tackled *without* a calculator – use a calculator to *check* your answers.

1) Add up
   a) 273, 86 and 5
   b) 9147, 502, 68 and 3
   c) 11856, 7320, 491, 79 and 4
   d) 126390, 87451, 6213, 504, 80 and 1
   e) 8223618, 740816, 51097, 6322, 417, 69 and 6

2) All the rows and columns in this diagram will add up to 150 if the numbers below are correctly placed. How should they be inserted?

	63	30	2	28
65				3
30		35		33
7				64
21	9	31	67	

The numbers are: 22, 25, 26, 26, 26, 27, 27, 27, 28 and 28.

3) In this diagram all the rows and columns will add up to 180 if the numbers below are correctly inserted. How should they be placed?

	50	40	13	
52				14
17				61
	21	32	60	

The numbers are: 33, 33, 34, 34, 34, 34, 35, 36, 37, 38, 38, 38, 38, 39 and 39.

Multiplication

Think of multiplication as a form of addition, where a number has the *same* number added to it, once or more times – thus it is doubled, trebled etc.

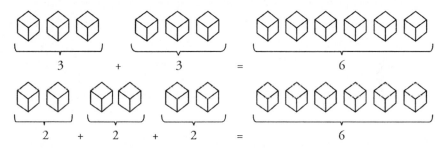

Like addition, multiplication is a process which *increases* the original number. It is essential to learn the multiplication tables up to 10 to make mental arithmetic perform well for you; if you don't know them already, spend a little time learning the table below.

1	2	3	4	5	6	7	8	9	10
2	4	6	8	10	12	14	16	18	20
3	6	9	12	15	18	21	24	27	30
4	8	12	16	20	24	28	32	36	40
5	10	15	20	25	30	35	40	45	50
6	12	18	24	30	36	42	48	54	60
7	14	21	28	35	42	49	56	63	70
8	16	24	32	40	48	56	64	72	80
9	18	27	36	45	54	63	72	81	90
10	20	30	40	50	60	70	80	90	100

The following table gives some quick tips for multiplication.

Multiply by:	Quick tip	Example
10	simply add a zero	$13 \times 10 = 130$
4	double and double again	21×4; $21 \times 2 = 42$, $42 \times 2 = 84$
5	halve the number and add a zero	94×5; half of 94 = 47, add a zero = 470
6	multiply by 3, then double	16×6; $16 \times 3 = 48$, $48 \times 2 = 96$
8	double, then double and double again	47×8; $47 \times 2 = 94$, $94 \times 2 = 188$, $188 \times 2 = 376$
9	add a zero and then subtract the original number	68×9; add a zero = 680, subtract 68 = 612
11	add a zero and add the original number	137×11; add a zero = 1370, add 137 = 1507
12	add a zero then add twice the original number	56×12, add a zero = 560, add 112 = 672

For a more complex multiplication, say 6483 multiplied by 157, the 'long multiplication' method is

$$
\begin{array}{r}
6483 \\
\times\,157 \\
\hline
648300 \\
324150 \\
45381 \\
\hline
1017831 \\
\end{array}
$$

The above is the same as splitting up the operation into three parts, thus:

$$
\begin{aligned}
6483 \times 157 &= 6483 \times 100 + 6483 \times 50 + 6483 \times 7 \\
&= 648300 + 324150 + 45381 \\
&= 1017831
\end{aligned}
$$

Multiplication Questions

4) Multiply:
   a) 92 × 7
   b) 923 × 74
   c) 9236 × 748
   d) 92361 × 7480
   e) 923615 × 74809

5) A theatre has 9 rows in the stalls, each row having 16 seats, 5 rows in the circle, each row having 22 seats and 4 rows in the gallery, each row having 14 seats. What is the seating capacity of the theatre?

The theatre sells all it's seats for a play. If the seat prices are £15 each for the stalls, £12 for the circle and £8 for the gallery, what are the takings for the performance?

Subtraction

Subtraction is the taking away of a number (or numbers) from a larger number to leave a smaller one.

$$5 - 3 = 2$$

Some quick tips are:

To subtract 9: subtract 10 and add 1
To subtract 8: subtract 10 and add 2
To subtract 7: subtract 10 and add 3

The above principle can be used for simple subtractions:

thus: $2076 - 38$
$$= 2076 - 40 + 2$$
$$= 2036 + 2$$
$$= \underline{2038}$$

and: $13954 - 112$
$$= 13954 - 110 - 2$$
$$= 13844 - 2$$
$$= \underline{13842}$$

For more complex subtractions, one way is to set then out in vertical columns

Thus: 401325 less 58609

```
 401325
  58609
```

Stage 1   in the right-hand column, we cannot take away 9 form 5, so it has to be 9 from 15, leaving 6

```
 401325
  58609
      6
```

Stage 2   in the next column, we have already taken 1 from 2, so it has to be 0 from 1, leaving 1

```
 401325
  58609
     16
```

Stage 3   as in stage 1, we sutbract 6 from 13, leaving 7

```
 401325
  58609
    716
```

Stage 4   again, we subtract 8 from 10, leaving 2

$$\begin{array}{r} 401325 \\ \underline{58609} \\ 2716 \end{array}$$

Stage 5   lastly, we subtract 5 from 39, leaving 34

$$\begin{array}{r} 401325 \\ \underline{58609} \\ \underline{342716} \end{array}$$

Check the final figure by adding it to the middle one – it should give you the top one.

Alternatively, one can subtract the thousands, hundreds, tens and digits separately.

Thus, in the above example:

$$401325 - 58609 = 401325 - 50000 - 8000 - 600 - 9$$
$$= 351325 - 8000 - 600 - 9$$
$$= 343325 - 600 - 9$$
$$= 342725 - 9$$
$$= \underline{342716}$$

If subtracting a series of numbers, bracket and add them together before subtraction.

Thus:

$$517244 - 10017 - 8376 - 529 - 63 = 517244 - (10017 + 8376 + 529 + 63)$$
$$= 517244 - 18985$$
$$= \underline{498259}$$

Subtraction questions

6) Subtract
   a) 9 from 86
   b) 23 from 157
   c) 409 from 2681
   d) 3176 from 50364
   e) 187 and 3013 from 4721

7) A motorist undertakes a 200 mile journey. He starts by travelling on a 4 mile long 'B' road, continues on an 'A' road which is 53 miles long before joining a motorway for a distance of 127 miles. He finally completes his journey on another 'A' road. What is the length of this road?

Division

Division is the splitting up of a number into smaller equal ones: thus 6 divided by 3 is 6 split into 3 groups of 2 or mathematically $\frac{6}{3} = 2$. Like subtraction, division is a process which *decreases* the value of the number.

Divisibility Rules

All even numbers are divisible by 2.

To check if a number is divisible by 3, first determine whether its digit sum is divisible by 3. The digit sum of a number is found by adding together its digits: e.g. the digit sum of 756 = 7 + 5 + 6 = 18, then 1 + 8 = 9, thus since its digit sum (9) is divisible by 3, we know that 756 is also divisible by 3.

All numbers ending in 5 or 0 are divisible by 5.

A number is divisible by 6 if it is also divisible by 2 and 3. So, it must be an even number which also has a digit sum which is a multiple of 3: e.g. 426 – an even number – has a digit sum of 12, then 3. We thus know that 426 is divisible by 6.

A number is always divisible by 9 if its digit sum is 9: e.g. 3618 = 3 + 6 + 1 + 8 = 18, 1 + 8 = 9. Therefore 3618 is divisible by 9.

A number is always divisible by 10 if it ends in zero.

For a more difficult division, say 2041542 divided by 351, use the 'long division' method.

$$
\begin{array}{r}
6842 \\
351 \overline{)\ 2401542} \\
\underline{2106} \\
2955 \\
\underline{2808} \\
1474 \\
\underline{1404} \\
702 \\
702
\end{array}
$$

First, multiply 351 by a digit to give the nearest number just below 2401; hence 351 × 6 = 2106, repeat this process three more times. To check the calculation, multiply the answer by 351.

Division Questions

8) a) Divide 1263 by 3.
  b) Divide 2648 by 4.
  c) Divide 3045 by 7.
  d) Divide 4336 by 8.
  e) Divide 5742 by 9.

9) A bar of chocolate has 32 squares. If the bar is divided up into 8 equal pieces, how many squares has each piece?

10) Divide 3201737 by 473.

11) You have £79.98 in your pocket, made up of five kinds of coin in current use. You have 93 of each coin. What is the value of each coin?

12) An example of addition, subtraction, multiplication and division.

Solve $\dfrac{178 \times 942 + 1038}{163 \times 527 - 29663}$

Supermarket Maths

Spending within one's budget can be done by keeping a 'running total' on your shopping list. In the example below the budget figure is £10.00 and the 'running total' – that is the immediate total in the right-hand column – is entered until up to the £10 limit.

	£	£
Coffee	4.35	4.35
Eggs	1.30	5.65
Butter	0.60	6.25
Baked Beans	0.30	6.55
Cheese	1.25	7.80
Chocolate	1.05	8.85
Apples	1.15	10.00

Alternatively, the cost of each purchase can be *subtracted* from the budget figure of £10.00 until down to zero.

	£	£
Coffee	4.35	5.65
Eggs	1.30	4.35
Butter	0.60	3.75
Baked Beans	0.30	3.45
Cheese	1.25	2.20
Chocolate	1.05	1.15
Apples	1.15	0.00

This is a simple way of keeping your mental arithmetic in good order – take a clipboard with you.

For any brand of product, be it jam, baked beans or coffee, the largest size will invariably be the cheapest – to check, work out the cost per 100 grams for each size. Also, the Supermarket's own brand of product will usually be cheaper than other brands – again, compare the cost per 100 grams.

Another worthwhile exercise is to check your monthly Bank Statements against entries in your Check Book – do this by subtracting STO and DDR payments from the balance shown in your Cheque Book.

Fractions, percentages and degrees

So far we have dealt with whole numbers – now we must consider parts of whole numbers.

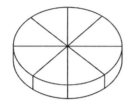

Imagine a circular cake cut into 8 equal slices. Each slice is an eighth (⅛), of the whole.

Similarly, if a tree trunk is sawn into 8 logs of equal length, each log is an eighth of the total length. An eighth or ⅛ is an ORDINARY FRACTION. (Also known as a VULGAR FRACTION).

It can also be expressed as a DECIMAL FRACTION: 1 divided by 8 = 0.125 or as a PERCENTAGE: ⅛ multiplied by 100 = 12.5%.

In an ordinary fraction, the number written above the line is the NUMERATOR and the number written below the line is the DENOMINATOR. Thus in the fraction ⅛, 1 is the numerator and 8 is the denominator. When adding or subtracting fractions, we have to find the LOWEST COMMON DENOMINATOR (LCD) which is the lowest number which can be divided by all the separate denominators.

Thus $\dfrac{1}{8} + \dfrac{1}{6} + \dfrac{1}{2} = \dfrac{3 + 4 + 12}{24} = \dfrac{19}{24}$; 24 being the LCD of 8, 6 and 2.

As the UK Imperial system of measures is being superseded by the Metric system, feet and inches are becoming metres, centimetres and millimetres, which makes sense since decimal fractions, unlike ordinary fractions, can be fed directly into calculators; e.g. 1 ft 2½ in = 368.3 millimetres.

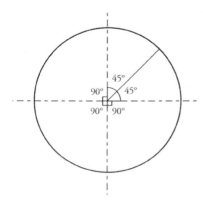

The circular cake, mentioned previously, can be split up into degrees: a complete circle comprising 360 degrees (360°)

If a circle is split up into 4 equal parts, each part is known as a right angle or an angle of 90°.

Similarly, the slices in our circular cake contain an angle of 45°.

Fractions percentages and degrees questions

13) Express
    a) ⅕ as a decimal fraction and as a percentage.
    b) 0.25 as an ordinary fraction and as a percentage.
    c) 40% as an ordinary fraction and as a decimal fraction.

14) What is the LCD of 9, 5 and 3?

15) Convert in one ordinary fraction

    a) $\dfrac{3}{7} + \dfrac{2}{9} + \dfrac{1}{3}$

    b) $\dfrac{1}{4} + \dfrac{5}{6} - \dfrac{1}{9}$

16) A circle is split up into 6 sectors; the included angles of 5 sectors are as shown in the diagram. What is the included angle of the sixth one?

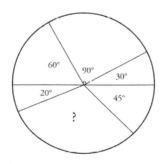

17) A man sets off to drive from one city to another. In the first hour he covers one quarter of the distance. In the second hour he travels one half of what is left and in the third hour one third of the remainder. In the fourth hour he covers one half of what is remaining and finds that he is 16 miles away. How many miles has he travelled so far?

Squares and cubes

The SQUARE of a number is the product obtained when a number is multiplied by itself; i.e. the square of 4 is 16 ($4 \times 4 = 16$).

It is used in the theorem of Pythagoras and the calculation of areas which we shall deal with later.

The CUBE of a number is the product of a number multiplied by itself twice; i.e. the cube of 3 is 27 ($3 \times 3 \times 3 = 27$).

It is used in the calculation of volumes.

Square roots and cube roots

A Square root is a number in relation to a given number which it produces when multiplied by itself once; i.e. 3 is the square root of 9 ($3 \times 3 = 9$).

A Cube root is a number in relation to a given number which it produces when multiplied by itself twice; i.e. 2 is a cube root of 8 ($2 \times 2 \times 2 = 8$).

In mathematical symbols: $\sqrt{9} = 3$ and $\sqrt[3]{8} = 2$.

Triangles

A Triangle is any three sided figure.

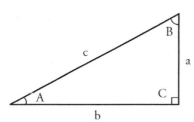

A common form is a right angled one – that is a triangle in which one of the angles is 90°. (C in the diagram)

With reference to angle A:
a = opposite side
b = adjacent side
c = hypotenuse

This is a convenient point to introduce a branch of mathematics known as ALGEBRA, which is simply expressing quantities in terms of letters and symbols.

In our right angled triangle above, by the theorem of Pythagoras (a sixth century Greek mathematician): $a^2 + b^2 = c^2$, or the square of the hypotenuse equals the sum of the squares of the two adjacent sides.

A common shape of right angled triangle is one having sides of length 3, 4 and 5, thus $3^2 + 4^2 = 9 + 16 = 25 = 5^2$.

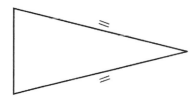

Isosceles Triangles have two equal sides.

Similar triangles are of identical shape but of different size.

Triangles ABC and ADE are similar. If AE, AC and DE are equal to 6, 10 and 3 and BC = X:

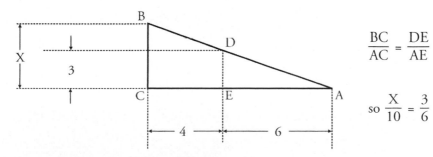

$$\frac{BC}{AC} = \frac{DE}{AE}$$

so $$\frac{X}{10} = \frac{3}{6}$$

Cross multiplying: $6X = 30$ and $\underline{X = 5}$.

17

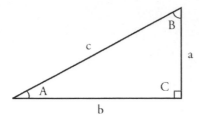

Another branch of mathematics is TRIGONOMETRY, which deals with the relationship between sides and angles of triangles. Referring to the right angled triangle above

$$\text{Sine } A = \frac{\text{opposite side}}{\text{hypotenuse}} = \frac{a}{c}$$

$$\text{Cosine } A = \frac{\text{adjacent side}}{\text{hypotenuse}} = \frac{b}{c}$$

$$\text{Tangent } A = \frac{\text{opposite side}}{\text{adjacent side}} = \frac{a}{b}$$

The Sine, Cosine and Tangent terms are abbreviated to Sin, Cos and Tan. So similarly:

$$\text{Sin } B = \frac{b}{c}$$

$$\text{Cos } B = \frac{a}{c}$$

$$\text{Tan } B = \frac{b}{a}$$

From the above equations:

$$\text{Sin}^2 A + \text{Cos}^2 A = \frac{a^2}{c^2} + \frac{b^2}{c^2} = \frac{a^2 + b^2}{c^2}$$

But, by Pythagoras, $a^2 + b^2 = c^2$

So, $\text{Sin}^2 A + \text{Cos}^2 A = 1$

In any triangle –

1) $\dfrac{a}{\text{Sin } A} = \dfrac{b}{\text{Sin } B} = \dfrac{c}{\text{Sin } C}$

2) $a^2 = b^2 + c^2 - 2bc \text{ Cos } A$

It is important to remember that the three angles of a triangle total 180°.

Triangle questions

18) *A Sightscreen for Glen McGrath*
A batsman is facing the bowling of the Australian. The batsman's eye level is 1.7m above ground level, the ball leaving the bowler's hand is 2.4 metres above the ground, the distance between batsman and bowler is 18 metres and the distance behind the bowler to the sightscreen is 180 metres. What minimum height of sightscreen is required for the batsman to be able to sight the ball properly?
Tip – First make a sketch showing the above dimensions when tackling this problem.

19) Calculate the length of AB and AC.

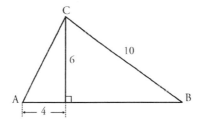

20) Calculate H.

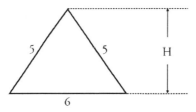

21) a) Calculate BC and Angles A and C.

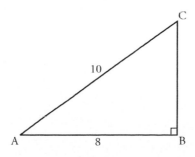

b) Calculate BC and Angle B.

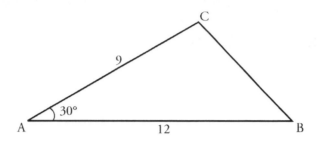

c) Calculate Angles A, B and C.

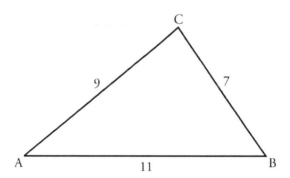

Circles

Definitions

Radius – r   The straight line distance between the centre of a circle and its circumference.

Diameter – d   The width of a circle - equal to twice the radius.

π   The Greek letter π - equals the ratio of the circumference of a circle to its diameter = 3.142.

Circumference   The circular distance around a circle = πd.

Arc   The *circular distance* between two points (A and B on the diagram) on the circumference of a circle.

Chord   The *straight distance* between two points (A and B on the diagram) on the circumference of a circle.

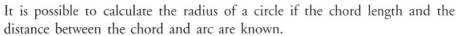

It is possible to calculate the radius of a circle if the chord length and the distance between the chord and arc are known.

If chord length = 2x
and distance between chord and arc = y

then in right angled triangle OBC, by Pythagoras,

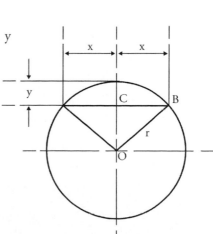

$$x^2 + (r - y)^2 = r^2$$

$$x^2 + r^2 - 2ry + y^2 = r^2$$

$$2ry = x^2 + y^2$$

$$r = \frac{x^2 + y^2}{2y}$$

Circle Questions

22) If the diameter of a circle is 2.5 metres, what is its circumference?

23) In the diagram, what is the length of the Arc AB and the chord AB?

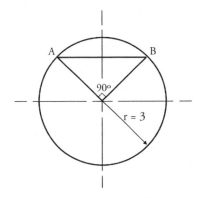

24) A circle has a chord length 12 and a distance between chord and arc of 3, what is it's radius? Draw a diagram before starting the calculation.

25) The captain of a ship is standing on the bridge of his vessel. If his eye level is 10 metres above sea level, how far can he see ahead on a clear day? (Assume the earth's diameter to be 12750 kilometres.) Again, draw a diagram before proceeding with the calculation.

Four-sided Figures

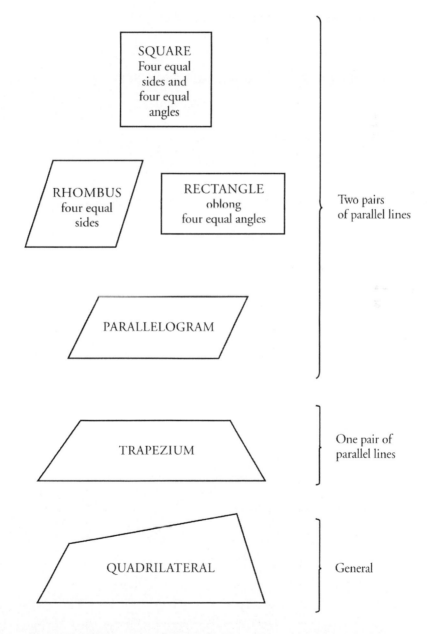

Remember that the 4 angles of a four sided figure always total 360°.

Four-sided figure questions

26) Calculate the diagonal length of –
   a) A 2 metre × 2 metre square.
   b) A 3 metre × 4 metre rectangle.

27) Calculate the length of the diagonals AC and BD of –

a) A Rhombus

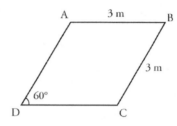

a) A parallelogram

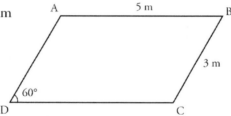

28) Calculate the length AB of –

a) A Trapezium

b) A Quadrilateral

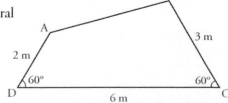

Areas

Area is the size of any two dimensional surface.

Triangles

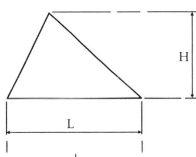

$A = \frac{1}{2} \times Base \times Height$
$= \frac{1}{2} LH$

Circles

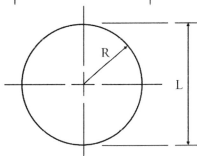

$A = \frac{\pi D^2}{4}$ or πR^2

Squares

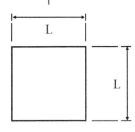

$A = L^2$

Rectangles

$A = LH$

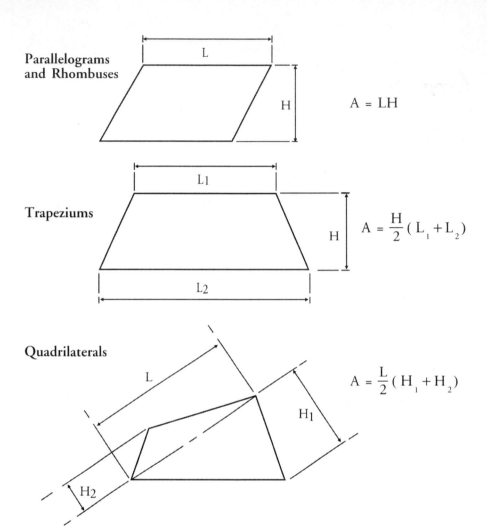

**Parallelograms
and Rhombuses**

$A = LH$

Trapeziums

$$A = \frac{H}{2}(L_1 + L_2)$$

Quadrilaterals

$$A = \frac{L}{2}(H_1 + H_2)$$

Area questions

29) Calculate the area of –

a)
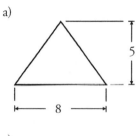

b)
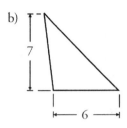

c)
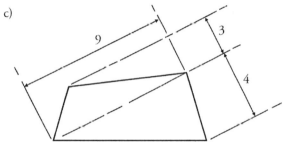

30) Calculate the area of –

a)
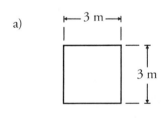

b)
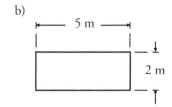

c)
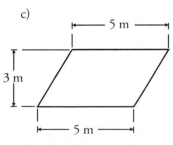

d)
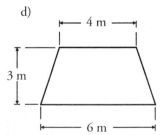

31) The flag of a shipping company consists of a black rhombus on a white rectangle, as shown in the diagram. The length of the rectangle is 1.4 m, the width is 0.7 m and the rhombus is made by joining the midpoints of the sides. Calculate the area of material required to make the rhombus.

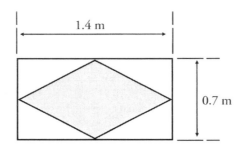

32) The diagram shows a 60° segment of a circle of radius R. If R = 1.5 m, calculate the areas of the triangle OAB and the segment OAB.

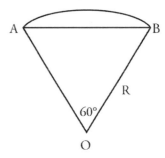

33) A DIY enthusiast is renovating a room by painting its walls and ceiling and laying a new carpet. The dimensions of the room are shown in the diagram.

   a) If 1 litre of emulsion covers 15 m², how much paint will be required?

   b) How much carpet will be required for the floor?

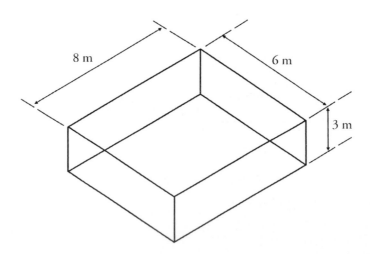

Volumes

Volume is the size of any three-dimensional object.

	Volume	*Surface area*

Cube

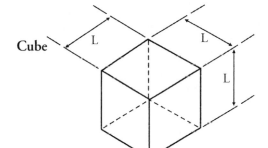

L^3 $6L^2$

Sphere

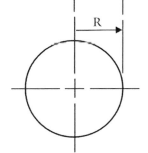

$\frac{4}{3} \pi R^3$ $4 \pi R^2$

Cone

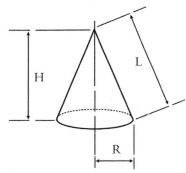

$\frac{1}{3} \pi R^2 H$ πRL

	Volume	*Surface area*

Cylinder

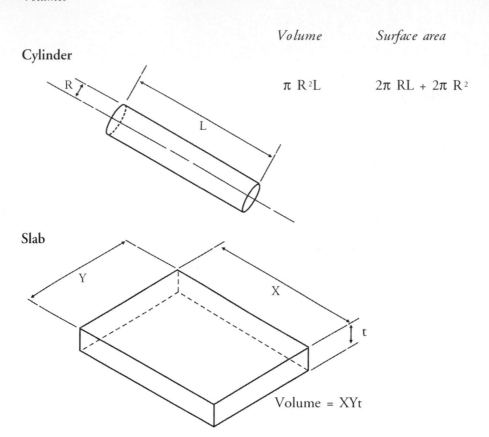

$\pi\ R^2L$ $2\pi\ RL\ +\ 2\pi\ R^2$

Slab

Volume = XYt

For bodies of uniform X-section; Volume = X-sectional area × length.
For bodies of uniform thickness; Volume = Surface area × depth.

Volume questions

34) Calculate the volume of –
  a) A brick – 225 mm × 112.5 mm × 75 mm.
  b) A sphere – 500 mm radius.
  c) A cone – 300 mm radius and 500 mm slant height.
  d) A round bar – 19 mm radius and 1m long.

35) A fan is being installed in a kitchen whose dimensions are 4 metres long × 3 metres wide × 2.5 metres high. If 15 air changes are required every hour, what size fan must be used?

36) Calculate the volume of the swimming pool whose dimensions are shown in the diagram.

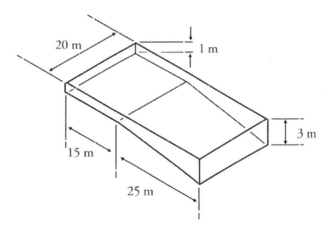

37) A waste oil container of 5 litre capacity is being filled by a conical funnel – dimensions as shown in the diagram. How many times must the funnel be filled to completely fill the oil container?

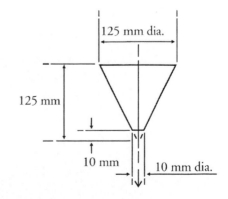

38) A new tube of shaving cream is roughly a cylinder of 3.0 cm diameter and 13.5 cm length. Calculate the volume of shaving cream in the tube (cm^3). The cream is squeezed through a circular hole of 7.5 mm diameter. Each time I shave I use a 'cylinder' of 27 mm length. How many shaves can I get from this tube?

Weights

If the volume of a body is known, its weight can be calculated if the *specific gravity* of the substance is known.

Specific gravity is the ratio between the weight of the substance and that of the same volume of water. The *specific gravity* of water is 1.00 and its weight/unit volume is 0.036 lb/cu in or 62.4 lb/cu ft.

The specific gravities and weights /unit volume of various common substances are as follows –

	Substance	Sp Gr	kg/cu metres	lb/cu in	lb/cu ft
Metals	Aluminium	2.64	2640	0.095	165
	Brass	8.56	8544	0,309	534
	Copper	8.89	8880	0.321	555
	Lead	11.35	11328	0.410	708
	Steel	7.80	7792	0.282	487
Building Materials	Brick – common	2.00	2000	0.072	125
	Cement – set	2.88	2880	0.104	180
	Concrete	2.00	2000	0.072	125
	Glass	2.63	2624	0.095	164
	Oak	0.86	864	0.031	54
	Pine	0.47	464	0.017	29
	Sand – dry, loose	1.61	1600	0.058	100
Fuels	Petrol	0.88	880	0.032	55
	Coal	1.36	1360	0.049	85
	Coke	0.50	496	0.018	31
Plastics	Nylon	1.25	1248	0.045	78
	Polyester	1.30	1296	0.047	81
	Polyethylene	0.94	944	0.034	59
	Polypropylene	0.91	912	0.033	57

Weight questions

39) The dimensions of a glass tumbler are as shown –

    Calculate the weight of the tumbler when
a) Empty.
b) Full of water.

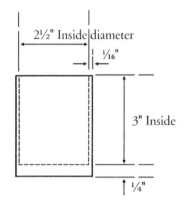

40) The diagram shows a steel Bearing Housing, with a brass bush at its centre.

Calculate its weight.

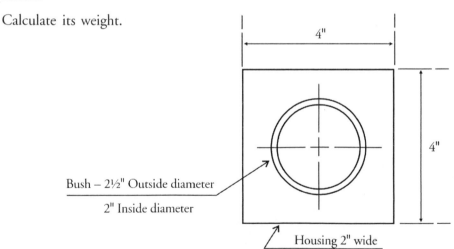

By how much will its weight be reduced if the brass bush is replaced by a nylon one?

41) In questions 41 and 42, metric dimensions and densities are used, the density of water being 1 gram/cubic centimetre. In the sketch below, the thermometer consists of mercury (shaded) enclosed in a sealed glass tube – all dimensions are in millimetres. Calculate the weight of the thermometer in grams. Assume that the Sp Grs of glass and mercury are 2.63 and 13.55 respectively.

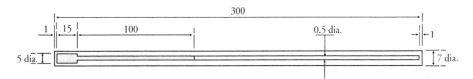

42) A table consists of a 800 × 800 × 15 mm wooden top (Sp Gr 0.47) covered by 3 mm thick plastic (Sp Gr 0.94). The top is supported on 4 legs – 700 mm long × 25 mm dia – made of wood (Sp Gr 0.86). Calculate the weight of the table in kilograms.

Speed and acceleration

Speed, or velocity, is the rate at which something moves or operates. It can apply to a solid (motor car), a liquid (water) or a gas (air).

For road rail or air transport, speed is usually in Miles per hour (mph), Kilometres per hour (kph), feet or metres per second.
  Thus 60 mph =100 kph = 88 feet pre second.

For sea and air transport, speed is measured in knots = nautical miles pre hour. 1 knot = 6076 feet per hour or 1.852 kilometres per hour.

Acceleration is the rate in time at which something increases in speed – conversely, *Deceleration* denotes the rate of decrease of speed.
  Acceleration and deceleration are normally measured in feet or metres per second per second.
  Thus, if a body accelerates uniformly from rest to 30 feet per second in 10 seconds, its acceleration is

$$\frac{\text{speed}}{\text{time}} = \frac{30}{10} = 3 \text{ feet per second per second or } \underline{3 \text{ ft/sec}^2}$$

Expressed as a formula:

$$v = u + ft, \text{ where } \left. \begin{array}{l} v = \text{final velocity} \\ u = \text{initial velocity} \\ f = \text{acceleration} \\ t = \text{time} \end{array} \right\}$$

Speed and acceleration questions

43) A train, which is 176 yards long, is travelling at a speed of 30 mph. It enters a tunnel which is one mile long. How long will it take for the whole train to pass through the tunnel? That is from the moment the engine enters the tunnel to the moment the last carriage emerges from it.

44) A bath, which can be considered to be a rectangular tank of dimensions 1.5m long × 0.6m wide × 0.4 m deep is being filled by a tap from which water issues at 0.02 m/min. How long will it take to half fill the bath?

45) A car approaching a town reduces speed from 60 mph to 30 mph in 10 seconds. What is its rate of deceleration?

46) *The space economy of public transport*
A bus, travelling on a motorway, is carrying 40 passengers and is 45 feet long. If the vehicle breaks down and the passengers are transferred to several cars, how much space (length of motorway) will they now occupy.
Assuming:
   a) Each car is 15 feet long and carries 4 people.
   b) There is a '2 second' gap between each car – '2 seconds' being the distance travelled in that time by the cars moving at 70 mph.

What is the ratio of $\dfrac{\text{space occupied by cars}}{\text{space occupied by bus}}$?

47) A car, 15 feet long, overtakes a stationary vehicle, 30 feet long. It moves out of its lane when it is 45 feet behind the stationary vehicle and reverts to its normal position when it is 45 feet ahead. If the car is travelling at 30 mph how long will the operation take?

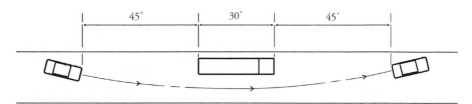

If the vehicle, stationary in the previous situation, is now travelling at 55 mph and the car at 60 mph, how long will the manoeuvre now take? How far will the car have travelled whilst overtaking?

Statistics

Statistics is a branch of mathematics which collects and interpolates data.

Probability is a ratio which estimates the chances that a certain event will occur.

Expressed as a formula, $P = \dfrac{A}{B}$

where

$\left.\begin{array}{l} P = \text{Probability} \\ A = \text{your desired outcome} \\ B = \text{total number of outcomes.} \end{array}\right\}$

In tossing a coin, the number of options are two – heads or tails.

$$\text{Thus } P = \frac{\text{heads}}{\text{heads} + \text{tails}} = \frac{1}{2} = \underline{50\%}$$

In throwing a dice, the probability of getting a six is

$$\frac{\text{a six (1)}}{\text{six numbers (6)}} = \underline{16.67\%}$$

$$\text{The Average or Mean figure} = \frac{\text{sum of quantities}}{\text{number of quantities}}$$

Thus, if in 8 Premier Football League matches:
$\left.\begin{array}{l} \text{In 2 matches, 6 goals are scored in each match,} \\ \text{in 3 matches, 5 goals are scored in each match,} \\ \text{in 2 matches, 2 goals are scored in each match,} \\ \text{and in 1 match, 1 goal is scored.} \end{array}\right\}$

The Average number of goals scored per match is

$$\frac{6 \times 2 + 5 \times 3 + 2 \times 2 + 1 \times 1}{2 + 3 + 2 + 1} = \frac{32}{8} = \underline{4}.$$

Data can conveniently be shown by various types of diagram:

1) *Graph* – a diagram, comprising a line or lines, showing the relationship between two quantities.
2) *Bar Chart* – a diagram, comprising of bars, showing the relationship between two quantities.
3) *Pie Chart* – a circle, divided into sections by radii, to show relative quantities or percentages.

Graph showing the cost of a three bedroom detatched house (£)

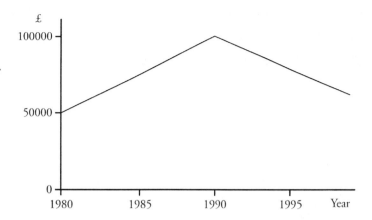

Bar charts showing the cost of a three bedroom detatched house (£)

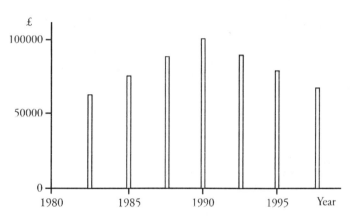

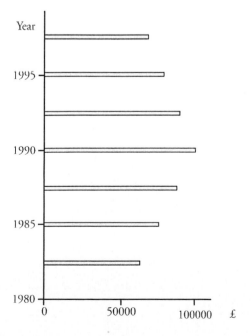

Statistics questions

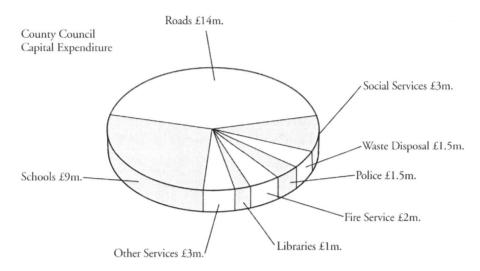

County Council
Capital Expenditure

Roads £14m.

Social Services £3m.

Waste Disposal £1.5m.

Police £1.5m.

Fire Service £2m.

Schools £9m.—

Other Services £3m.

Libraries £1m.

48) In the pie chart above, showing the County Council Capital Expenditure, express the eight separate expenditures as percentages of the total expenditure.

49) The Salaries of 6 employees working in a company are as follows – £21,000, £15,000, £19,000, £17,000, £33,500 and £26,500. What is their Average Salary?

50) A toilet roll is 12cm outside diameter and 5 cm inside diameter. If the toilet paper of 0.125 mm thick, what is the total length of paper on the roll?

Conversion factors

IMPERIAL WITH METRIC EQUIVALENTS		METRIC WITH IMPERIAL EQUIVALENTS	
Linear measure			
1 inch	= 25.4 millimetres	1 millimetre	= 0.039 inches
1 foot = 12 inches	= 0.3048 metre	1 centimetre = 10 mm	= 0.0394 inches
1 yard = 3 feet	= 0.9144 metre	1 metre = 100 cm	= 1.094 yards
1 mile = 1760 yards	= 1.609 kilometres	1 kilometre = 1000 m	= 0.6214 miles
Square measure			
1 square inch	= 6.45 square centimetres	1 square centimetre	= 0.155 square inches
1 square foot = 144 square inches	= 928.8 square centimetres	1 square metre = 10,000 square centimetres	= 1.196 square yards
1 square yard = 9 square feet	= 0.836 square metres	1 hectare = 100,000 square metres	= 2.471 acres
1 acre = 4840 square yards	= 0.405 hectares		
Cubic measure			
1 cubic inch	= 16.4 cubic centimetres	1 cubic centimetre	= 0.061 cubic inches
I cubic foot = 1,728 cubic inches	= 0.0283 cubic metres	1 cubic metre	= 1.308 cubic yards
1 cubic yard = 27 cubic feet	= 0.765 cubic metres		
Capacity measure			
1 gallon = 8 pints	= 4.546 litres	1 litre = 1.76 pints	= 0.22 gallons

Weight

1 ounce	= 28.35 grams	1 kilogram	= 2.205 pounds
		= 1000 grams	
1 pound	= 453.6 grams	1 tonne	= 0.984 ton
= 16 ounces		= 1000 kilograms	
1 ton	= 1.016 tonnes		
= 2240 pounds			

Temperature

On the Fahrenheit Scale – water boils at 212° and freezes at 32°.

On the Celsius or Centigrade Scale – water boils at 100° and freezes at 0°.

$$°F = \frac{°C \times 9}{5} + 32$$

$$°C = (°F - 32) \times \frac{5}{9}$$

Mathematical Symbols

+	Plus or Add	θ	Any angle
−	Minus or Subtract	∠	Angle
±	Plus or Minus	∟	Right Angle (90°)
×	Multiply by	∝	Proportional to
÷	Divide by	∞	Infinity
=	Equal to	‖	Parallel to
∴	Therefore	∦	Not Parallel to
<	Less than	⊥	Perpendicular to
>	Greater than	√	Square Root
≮	Not Less than	∛	Cube Root
≯	Not Greater than	( )²	Number squared
Σ	Sum of the terms	( )³	Number cubed

Algebraic multiplication

$$(a + b)^2 = (a + b)\,a + (a + b)\,b$$
$$= a^2 + ab + ab + b^2$$
$$= \underline{a^2 + 2ab + b^2}$$
$$(a - b)^2 = (a - b)\,a - (a - b)\,b$$
$$= a^2 - ab - ab + b^2$$
$$= \underline{a^2 - 2ab + b^2}$$
$$(a + b)\,(a - b) = (a + b)\,a - (a + b)\,b$$
$$= a^2 + ab - ab - b^2$$
$$= \underline{a^2 - b^2}$$

Remember that two *minus* numbers multiplied together make a *plus* and that a *minus* number and a *plus* number multiplied together make a *minus*.

CROSS MULTIPLICATION is a useful algebraic exercise:

If $\dfrac{A}{3} = \dfrac{B}{4}$: cross multiplying: $4A = 3B$ or $A = 0.75B$.

Checking with numbers:

$$\frac{2}{4} = \frac{1}{2} : 2 \times 2 = 4 \times 1 = 4$$

Compound Interest

This determines the growth of capital when invested in a bank or building society savings account. At the end of each year this interest is added to the starting capital to form a new capital figure.

Thus, if £1,000 is invested in an account giving 5% interest,

Capital at the end of the first year $\quad = 1000 \times 1.05 = £1050.00$

Capital at the end of the second year $\quad = 1050 \times 1.05 = £1102.50$

Capital at the end of the third year $\quad = 1102.50 \times 1.05 = £1157.62$

and so on.

Natural Sines

Degrees	0' 0°.0	6' 0°.1	12' 0°.2	18' 0°.3	24' 0°.4	30' 0°.5	36' 0°.6	42' 0°.7	48' 0°.8	54' 0°.9	Mean Differences 1	2	3	4	5
0	·0000	0017	0035	0052	0070	0087	0105	0122	0140	0157	3	6	9	12	15
1	·0175	0192	0209	0227	0244	0262	0279	0297	0314	0332	3	6	9	12	15
2	·0349	0366	0384	0401	0419	0436	0454	0471	0488	0506	3	6	9	12	15
3	·0523	0541	0558	0576	0593	0610	0628	0645	0663	0680	3	6	9	12	15
4	·0698	0715	0732	0750	0767	0785	0802	0819	0837	0854	3	6	9	12	15
5	·0872	0889	0906	0924	0941	0958	0976	0993	1011	1028	3	6	9	12	14
6	·1045	1063	1080	1097	1115	1132	1149	1167	1184	1201	3	6	9	12	14
7	·1219	1236	1253	1271	1288	1305	1323	1340	1357	1374	3	6	9	12	14
8	·1392	1409	1426	1444	1461	1478	1495	1513	1530	1547	3	6	9	12	14
9	·1564	1582	1599	1616	1633	1650	1668	1685	1702	1719	3	6	9	12	14
10	·1736	1754	1771	1788	1805	1822	1840	1857	1874	1891	3	6	9	12	14
11	·1908	1925	1942	1959	1977	1994	2011	2028	2045	2062	3	6	9	11	14
12	·2079	2096	2113	2130	2147	2164	2181	2198	2215	2232	3	6	9	11	14
13	·2250	2267	2284	2300	2317	2334	2351	2368	2385	2402	3	6	8	11	14
14	·2419	2436	2453	2470	2487	2504	2521	2538	2554	2571	3	6	8	11	14
15	·2588	2605	2622	2639	2656	2672	2689	2706	2723	2740	3	6	8	11	14
16	·2756	2773	2790	2807	2823	2840	2857	2874	2890	2907	3	6	8	11	14
17	·2924	2940	2957	2974	2990	3007	3024	3040	3057	3074	3	6	8	11	14
18	·3090	3107	3123	3140	3156	3173	3190	3206	3223	3239	3	6	8	11	14
19	·3256	3272	3289	3305	3322	3338	3355	3371	3387	3404	3	5	8	11	14
20	·3420	3437	3453	3469	3486	3502	3518	3535	3551	3567	3	5	8	11	14
21	·3584	3600	3616	3633	3649	3665	3681	3697	3714	3730	3	5	8	11	14
22	·3746	3762	3778	3795	3811	3827	3843	3859	3875	3891	3	5	8	11	14
23	·3907	3923	3939	3955	3971	3987	4003	4019	4035	4051	3	5	8	11	14
24	·4067	4083	4099	4115	4131	4147	4163	4179	4195	4210	3	5	8	11	13
25	·4226	4242	4258	4274	4289	4305	4321	4337	4352	4368	3	5	8	11	13
26	·4384	4399	4415	4431	4446	4462	4478	4493	4509	4524	3	5	8	10	13
27	·4540	4555	4571	4586	4602	4617	4633	4648	4664	4679	3	5	8	10	13
28	·4695	4710	4726	4741	4756	4772	4787	4802	4818	4833	3	5	8	10	13
29	·4848	4863	4879	4894	4909	4924	4939	4955	4970	4985	3	5	8	10	13
30	·5000	5015	5030	5045	5060	5075	5090	5105	5120	5135	3	5	8	10	13
31	·5150	5165	5180	5195	5210	5225	5240	5255	5270	5284	2	5	7	10	12
32	·5299	5314	5329	5344	5358	5373	5388	5402	5417	5432	2	5	7	10	12
33	·5446	5461	5476	5490	5505	5519	5534	5548	5563	5577	2	5	7	10	12
34	·5592	5606	5621	5635	5650	5664	5678	5693	5707	5721	2	5	7	10	12
35	·5736	5750	5764	5779	5793	5807	5821	5835	5850	5864	2	5	7	10	12
36	·5878	5892	5906	5920	5934	5948	5962	5976	5990	6004	2	5	7	9	12
37	·6018	6032	6046	6060	6074	6088	6101	6115	6129	6143	2	5	7	9	12
38	·6157	6170	6184	6198	6211	6225	6239	6252	6266	6280	2	5	7	9	11
39	·6293	6307	6320	6334	6347	6361	6374	6388	6401	6414	2	4	7	9	11
40	·6428	6441	6455	6468	6481	6494	6508	6521	6534	6547	2	4	7	9	11
41	·6561	6574	6587	6600	6613	6626	6639	6652	6665	6678	2	4	7	9	11
42	·6691	6704	6717	6730	6743	6756	6769	6782	6794	6807	2	4	6	9	11
43	·6820	6833	6845	6858	6871	6884	6896	6909	6921	6934	2	4	6	8	11
44	·6947	6959	6972	6984	6997	7009	7022	7034	7046	7059	2	4	6	8	10

Natural Sines

	0′	6′	12′	18′	24′	30′	36′	42′	48′	54′	2	4	6	8	10
45	·7071	7083	7096	7108	7120	7133	7145	7157	7169	7181	2	4	6	8	10
46	·7193	7206	7218	7230	7242	7254	7266	7278	7290	7302	2	4	6	8	10
47	·7314	7325	7337	7349	7361	7373	7385	7396	7408	7420	2	4	6	8	10
48	·7431	7443	7455	7466	7478	7490	7501	7513	7524	7536	2	4	6	8	10
49	·7547	7558	7570	7581	7593	7604	7615	7627	7638	7649	2	4	6	8	9
50	·7660	7672	7683	7694	7705	7716	7727	7738	7749	7760	2	4	6	7	9
51	·7771	7782	7793	7804	7815	7826	7837	7848	7859	7869	2	4	5	7	9
52	·7880	7891	7902	7912	7923	7934	7944	7955	7965	7976	2	4	5	7	9
53	·7986	7997	8007	8018	8028	8039	8049	8059	8070	8080	2	3	5	7	9
54	·8090	8100	8111	8121	8131	8141	8151	8161	8171	8181	2	3	5	7	8
55	·8192	8202	8211	8221	8231	8241	8251	8261	8271	8281	2	3	5	7	8
56	·8290	8300	8310	8320	8329	8339	8348	8358	8368	8377	2	3	5	6	8
57	·8387	8396	8406	8415	8425	8434	8443	8453	8462	8471	2	3	5	6	8
58	·8480	8490	8499	8508	8517	8526	8536	8545	8554	8563	2	3	5	6	8
59	·8572	8581	8590	8599	8607	8616	8625	8634	8643	8652	1	3	4	6	7
60	·8660	8669	8678	8686	8695	8704	8712	8721	8729	8738	1	3	4	6	7
61	·8746	8755	8763	8771	8780	8788	8796	8805	8813	8821	1	3	4	6	7
62	·8829	8838	8846	8854	8862	8870	8878	8886	8894	8902	1	3	4	5	7
63	·8910	8918	8926	8934	8942	8949	8957	8965	8973	8980	1	3	4	5	6
64	·8988	8996	9003	9011	9018	9026	9033	9041	9048	9056	1	3	4	5	6
65	·9063	9070	9078	9085	9092	9100	9107	9114	9121	9128	1	2	4	5	5
66	·9135	9143	9150	9157	9164	9171	9178	9184	9191	9198	1	2	3	5	6
67	·9205	9212	9219	9225	9232	9239	9245	9252	9259	9265	1	2	3	4	6
68	·9272	9278	9285	9291	9298	9304	9311	9317	9323	9330	1	2	3	4	5
69	·9336	9342	9348	9354	9361	9367	9373	9379	9385	9391	1	2	3	4	5
70	·9397	9403	9409	9415	9421	9426	9432	9438	9444	9449	1	2	3	4	5
71	·9455	9461	9466	9472	9478	9483	9489	9494	9500	9505	1	2	3	4	5
72	·9511	9516	9521	9527	9532	9537	9542	9548	9553	9558	1	2	3	3	4
73	·9563	9568	9573	9578	9583	9588	9593	9598	9603	9608	1	2	2	3	4
74	·9613	9617	9622	9627	9632	9636	9641	9646	9650	9655	1	2	2	3	4
75	·9659	9664	9668	9673	9677	9681	9686	9690	9694	9699	1	1	2	3	4
76	·9703	9707	9711	9715	9720	9724	9728	9732	9736	9740	1	1	2	3	3
77	·9744	9748	9751	9755	9759	9763	9767	9770	9774	9778	1	1	2	3	3
78	·9781	9785	9789	9792	9796	9799	9803	9806	9810	9813	1	1	2	2	3
79	·9816	9820	9823	9826	9829	9833	9836	9839	9842	9845	1	1	2	2	3
80	·9848	9851	9854	9857	9860	9863	9866	9869	9871	9874	0	1	1	2	2
81	·9877	9880	9882	9885	9888	9890	9893	9895	9898	9900	0	1	1	2	2
82	·9903	9905	9907	9910	9912	9914	9917	9919	9921	9923	0	1	1	2	2
83	·9925	9928	9930	9932	9934	9936	9938	9940	9942	9943	0	1	1	1	2
84	·9945	9947	9949	9951	9952	9954	9956	9957	9959	9960	0	1	1	1	2
85	·9962	9963	9965	9966	9968	9969	9971	9972	9973	9974	0	0	1	1	1
86	·9976	9977	9978	9979	9980	9981	9982	9983	9984	9985	0	0	1	1	1
87	·9986	9987	9988	9989	9990	9990	9991	9992	9993	9993	0	0	0	1	1
88	·9994	9995	9995	9996	9996	9997	9997	9997	9998	9998	0	0	0	0	0
89	·9998	9999	9999	9999	9999	1·000	1·000	1·000	1·000	1·000	0	0	0	0	0
90	1·000														

Natural Cosines

Degrees	0' 0°·0	6' 0°·1	12' 0°·2	18' 0°·3	24' 0°·4	30' 0°·5	36' 0°·6	42' 0°·7	48' 0°·8	54' 0°·9	Mean Differences 1	2	3	4	5
0	1·000	1·000	1·000	1·000	1·000	1·000	·9999	9999	9999	9999	0	0	0	0	0
1	·9998	9998	9998	9997	9997	9997	9996	9996	9995	9995	0	0	0	0	0
2	·9994	9993	9993	9992	9991	9990	9990	9989	9988	9987	0	0	0	1	1
3	·9986	9985	9984	9983	9982	9981	9980	9979	9978	9977	0	0	1	1	1
4	·9976	9974	9973	9972	9971	9969	9968	9966	9965	9963	0	0	1	1	1
5	·9962	9960	9959	9957	9956	9954	9952	9951	9949	9947	0	1	1	1	2
6	·9945	9943	9942	9940	9938	9936	9934	9932	9930	9928	0	1	1	1	2
7	·9925	9923	9921	9919	9917	9914	9912	9910	9907	9905	0	1	1	2	2
8	·9903	9900	9898	9895	9893	9890	9888	9885	9882	9880	0	1	1	2	2
9	·9877	9874	9871	9869	9866	9863	9860	9857	9854	9851	0	1	1	2	2
10	·9848	9845	9842	9839	9836	9833	9829	9826	9823	9820	1	1	2	2	3
11	·9816	9813	9810	9806	9803	9799	9796	9792	9789	9785	1	1	2	2	3
12	·9781	9778	9774	9770	9767	9763	9759	9755	9751	9748	1	1	2	3	3
13	·9744	9740	9736	9732	9728	9724	9720	9715	9711	9707	1	1	2	3	3
14	·9703	9699	9694	9690	9686	9681	9677	9673	9668	9664	1	1	2	3	4
15	·9659	9655	9650	9646	9641	9636	9632	9627	9622	9617	1	2	2	3	4
16	·9613	9608	9603	9598	9593	9588	9583	9578	9573	9568	1	2	2	3	4
17	·9563	9558	9553	9548	9542	9537	9532	9527	9521	9516	1	2	3	3	4
18	·9511	9505	9500	9494	9489	9483	9478	9472	9466	9461	1	2	3	4	5
19	·9455	9449	9444	9438	9432	9426	9421	9415	9409	9403	1	2	3	4	5
20	·9397	9391	9385	9379	9373	9367	9361	9354	9348	9342	1	2	3	4	5
21	·9336	9330	9323	9317	9311	9304	9298	9291	9285	9278	1	2	3	4	5
22	·9272	9265	9259	9252	9245	9239	9232	9225	9219	9212	1	2	3	4	6
23	·9205	9198	9191	9184	9178	9171	9164	9157	9150	9143	1	2	3	5	6
24	·9135	9128	9121	9114	9107	9100	9092	9085	9078	9070	1	2	4	5	6
25	·9063	9056	9048	9041	9033	9026	9018	9011	9003	8996	1	3	4	5	6
26	·8988	8980	8973	8965	8957	8949	8942	8934	8926	8918	1	3	4	5	6
27	·8910	8902	8894	8886	8878	8870	8862	8854	8846	8838	1	3	4	5	7
28	·8829	8821	8813	8805	8796	8788	8780	8771	8763	8755	1	3	4	6	7
29	·8746	8738	8729	8721	8712	8704	8695	8686	8678	8669	1	3	4	6	7
30	·8660	8652	8643	8634	8625	8616	8607	8599	8590	8581	1	3	4	6	7
31	·8572	8563	8554	8545	8536	8526	8517	8508	8499	8490	2	3	5	6	8
32	·8480	8471	8462	8453	8443	8434	8425	8415	8406	8396	2	3	5	6	8
33	·8387	8377	8368	8358	8348	8339	8329	8320	8310	8300	2	3	5	6	8
34	·8290	8281	8271	8261	8251	8241	8231	8221	8211	8202	2	3	5	7	8
35	·8192	8181	8171	8161	8151	8141	8131	8121	8111	8100	2	3	5	7	8
36	·8090	8080	8070	8059	8049	8039	8028	8018	8007	7997	2	3	5	7	9
37	·7986	7976	7965	7955	7944	7934	7923	7912	7902	7891	2	4	5	7	9
38	·7880	7869	7859	7848	7837	7826	7815	7804	7793	7782	2	4	5	7	9
39	·7771	7760	7749	7738	7727	7716	7705	7694	7683	7672	2	4	6	7	9
40	·7660	7649	7638	7627	7615	7604	7593	7581	7570	7559	2	4	6	8	9
41	·7547	7536	7524	7513	7501	7490	7478	7466	7455	7443	2	4	6	8	10
42	·7431	7420	7408	7396	7385	7373	7361	7349	7337	7325	2	4	6	8	10
43	·7314	7302	7290	7278	7266	7254	7242	7230	7218	7206	2	4	6	8	10
44	·7193	7181	7169	7157	7145	7133	7120	7108	7096	7083	2	4	6	8	10

Natural Cosines

	0′	6′	12′	18′	24′	30′	36′	42′	48′	54′	2	4	6	8	10
45	·7071	7059	7046	7034	7022	7009	6997	6984	6972	6959	2	4	6	8	10
46	·6947	6934	6921	6909	6896	6884	6871	6858	6845	6833	2	4	6	8	11
47	·6820	6807	6794	6782	6769	6756	6743	6730	6717	6704	2	4	6	9	11
48	·6691	6678	6665	6652	6639	6626	6613	6600	6587	6574	2	4	7	9	11
49	·6561	6547	6534	6521	6508	6494	6481	6468	6455	6441	2	4	7	9	11
50	·6428	6414	6401	6388	6374	6361	6347	6334	6320	6307	2	4	7	9	11
51	·6293	6280	6266	6252	6239	6225	6211	6198	6184	6170	2	5	7	9	11
52	·6157	6143	6129	6115	6101	6088	6074	6060	6046	6032	2	5	7	9	12
53	·6018	6004	5990	5976	5962	5948	5934	5920	5906	5892	2	5	7	9	12
54	·5878	5864	5850	5835	5821	5807	5793	5779	5764	5750	2	5	7	9	12
55	·5736	5721	5707	5693	5678	5664	5650	5635	5621	5606	2	5	7	10	12
56	·5592	5577	5563	5548	5534	5519	5505	5490	5476	5461	2	5	7	10	12
57	·5446	5432	5417	5402	5388	5373	5358	5344	5329	5314	2	5	7	10	12
58	·5299	5284	5270	5255	5240	5225	5210	5195	5180	5165	2	5	7	10	12
59	·5150	5135	5120	5105	5090	5075	5060	5045	5030	5015	3	5	8	10	13
60	·5000	4985	4970	4955	4939	4924	4909	4894	4879	4863	3	5	8	10	13
61	·4848	4833	4818	4802	4787	4772	4756	4741	4726	4710	3	5	8	10	13
62	·4695	4679	4664	4648	4633	4617	4602	4586	4571	4555	3	5	8	10	13
63	·4540	4524	4509	4493	4478	4462	4446	4431	4415	4399	3	5	8	10	13
64	·4384	4368	4352	4337	4321	4305	4289	4274	4258	4242	3	5	8	11	13
65	·4226	4210	4195	4179	4163	4147	4131	4115	4099	4083	3	5	8	11	13
66	·4067	4051	4035	4019	4003	3987	3971	3955	3939	3923	3	5	8	11	14
67	·3907	3891	3875	3859	3843	3827	3811	3795	3778	3762	3	5	8	11	14
68	·3746	3730	3714	3697	3681	3665	3649	3633	3616	3600	3	5	8	11	14
69	·3584	3567	3551	3535	3518	3502	3486	3469	3453	3437	3	5	8	11	14
70	·3420	3404	3387	3371	3355	3338	3322	3305	3289	3272	3	5	8	11	14
71	·3256	3239	3223	3206	3190	3173	3156	3140	3123	3107	3	6	8	11	14
72	·3090	3074	3057	3040	3024	3007	2990	2974	2957	2940	3	6	8	11	14
73	·2924	2907	2890	2874	2857	2840	2823	2807	2790	2773	3	6	8	11	14
74	·2756	2740	2723	2706	2689	2672	2656	2639	2622	2605	3	6	8	11	14
75	·2588	2571	2554	2538	2521	2504	2487	2470	2453	2436	3	6	8	11	14
76	·2419	2402	2385	2368	2351	2334	2317	2300	2284	2267	3	6	8	11	14
77	·2250	2233	2215	2198	2181	2164	2147	2130	2113	2096	3	6	9	11	14
78	·2079	2062	2045	2028	2011	1994	1977	1959	1942	1925	3	6	9	11	14
79	·1908	1891	1874	1857	1840	1822	1805	1788	1771	1754	3	6	9	11	14
80	·1736	1719	1702	1685	1668	1650	1633	1616	1599	1582	3	6	9	12	14
81	·1564	1547	1530	1513	1495	1478	1461	1444	1426	1409	3	6	9	12	14
82	·1392	1374	1357	1340	1323	1305	1288	1271	1253	1236	3	6	9	12	14
83	·1219	1201	1184	1167	1149	1132	1115	1097	1080	1063	3	6	9	12	14
84	·1045	1028	1011	0993	0976	0958	0941	0924	0906	0889	3	6	9	12	14
85	·0872	0854	0837	0819	0802	0785	0767	0750	0732	0715	3	6	9	12	15
86	·0698	0680	0663	0645	0628	0610	0593	0576	0558	0541	3	6	9	12	15
87	·0523	0506	0488	0471	0454	0436	0419	0401	0384	0366	3	6	9	12	15
88	·0349	0332	0314	0297	0279	0262	0244	0227	0209	0192	3	6	9	12	15
89	·0175	0157	0140	0122	0105	0087	0070	0052	0035	0017	3	6	9	12	15
90	·0000														

Natural Tangents

Degrees	0' 0'·0	6' 0'·1	12' 0'·2	18' 0'·3	24' 0'·4	30' 0'·5	36' 0'·6	42' 0'·7	48' 0'·8	54' 0'·9	1	2	3	4	5
0	·0000	0017	0035	0052	0070	0087	0105	0122	0140	0157	3	6	9	12	15
1	·0175	0192	0209	0227	0244	0262	0279	0297	0314	0332	3	6	9	12	15
2	·0349	0367	0384	0402	0419	0437	0454	0472	0489	0507	3	6	9	12	15
3	·0524	0542	0559	0577	0594	0612	0629	0647	0664	0682	3	6	9	12	15
4	·0699	0717	0734	0752	0769	0787	0805	0822	0840	0857	3	6	9	12	15
5	·0875	0892	0910	0928	0945	0963	0981	0998	1016	1033	3	6	9	12	15
6	·1051	1069	1086	1104	1122	1139	1157	1175	1192	1210	3	6	9	12	15
7	·1228	1246	1263	1281	1299	1317	1334	1352	1370	1388	3	6	9	12	15
8	·1405	1423	1441	1459	1477	1495	1512	1530	1548	1566	3	6	9	12	15
9	·1584	1602	1620	1638	1655	1673	1691	1709	1727	1745	3	6	9	12	15
10	·1763	1781	1799	1817	1835	1853	1871	1890	1908	1926	3	6	9	12	15
11	·1944	1962	1980	1998	2016	2035	2053	2071	2089	2107	3	6	9	12	15
12	·2126	2144	2162	2180	2199	2217	2235	2254	2272	2290	3	6	9	12	15
13	·2309	2327	2345	2364	2382	2401	2419	2438	2456	2475	3	6	9	12	15
14	·2493	2512	2530	2549	2568	2586	2605	2623	2642	2661	3	6	9	12	16
15	·2679	2698	2717	2736	2754	2773	2792	2811	2830	2849	3	6	9	13	16
16	·2867	2886	2905	2924	2943	2962	2981	3000	3019	3038	3	6	9	13	16
17	·3057	3076	3096	3115	3134	3153	3172	3191	3211	3230	3	6	10	13	16
18	·3249	3269	3288	3307	3327	3346	3365	3385	3404	3424	3	6	10	13	16
19	·3443	3463	3482	3502	3522	3541	3561	3581	3600	3620	3	7	10	13	16
20	·3640	3659	3679	3699	3719	3739	3759	3779	3799	3819	3	7	10	13	17
21	·3839	3859	3879	3899	3919	3939	3959	3979	4000	4020	3	7	10	13	17
22	·4040	4061	4081	4101	4122	4142	4163	4183	4204	4224	3	7	10	14	17
23	·4245	4265	4286	4307	4327	4348	4369	4390	4411	4431	3	7	10	14	17
24	·4452	4473	4494	4515	4536	4557	4578	4599	4621	4642	4	7	11	14	18
25	·4663	4684	4706	4727	4748	4770	4791	4813	4834	4856	4	7	11	14	18
26	·4877	4899	4921	4942	4964	4986	5008	5029	5051	5073	4	7	11	15	18
27	·5095	5117	5139	5161	5184	5206	5228	5250	5272	5295	4	7	11	15	18
28	·5317	5340	5362	5384	5407	5430	5452	5475	5498	5520	4	8	11	15	19
29	·5543	5566	5589	5612	5635	5658	5681	5704	5727	5750	4	8	12	15	19
30	·5774	5797	5820	5844	5867	5890	5914	5938	5961	5985	4	8	12	16	20
31	·6009	6032	6056	6080	6104	6128	6152	6176	6200	6224	4	8	12	16	20
32	·6249	6273	6297	6322	6346	6371	6395	6420	6445	6469	4	8	12	16	20
33	·6494	6519	6544	6569	6594	6619	6644	6669	6694	6720	4	8	13	17	21
34	·6745	6771	6796	6822	6847	6873	6899	6924	6950	6976	4	9	13	17	21
35	·7002	7028	7054	7080	7107	7133	7159	7186	7212	7239	4	9	13	18	22
36	·7265	7292	7319	7346	7373	7400	7427	7454	7481	7508	5	9	14	18	23
37	·7536	7563	7590	7618	7646	7673	7701	7729	7757	7785	5	9	14	18	23
38	·7813	7841	7869	7898	7926	7954	7983	8012	8040	8069	5	9	14	19	24
39	·8098	8127	8156	8185	8214	8243	8273	8302	8332	8361	5	10	15	20	24
40	·8391	8421	8451	8481	8511	8541	8571	8601	8632	8662	5	10	15	20	25
41	·8693	8724	8754	8785	8816	8847	8878	8910	8941	8972	5	10	16	21	26
42	·9004	9036	9067	9099	9131	9163	9195	9228	9260	9293	5	11	16	21	27
43	·9325	9358	9391	9424	9457	9490	9523	9556	9590	9623	6	11	17	22	28
44	·9657	9691	9725	9759	9793	9827	9861	9896	9930	9965	6	11	17	23	29

Natural Tangents

	0	6	12	18	24	30	36	42	48	54	1′2′3′	4′5′
45	1·0000	0035	0070	0105	0141	0176	0212	0247	0283	0319	6 12 18	24 30
46	1·0355	0392	0428	0464	0501	0538	0575	0612	0649	0686	6 12 18	25 31
47	1·0724	0761	0799	0837	0875	0913	0951	0990	1028	1067	6 13 19	25 32
48	1·1106	1145	1184	1224	1263	1303	1343	1383	1423	1463	7 13 20	27 33
49	1·1504	1544	1585	1626	1667	1708	1750	1792	1833	1875	7 14 21	28 34
50	1·1918	1960	2002	2045	2088	2131	2174	2218	2261	2305	7 14 22	29 36
51	1·2349	2393	2437	2482	2527	2572	2617	2662	2708	2753	8 15 23	30 38
52	1·2799	2846	2892	2938	2985	3032	3079	3127	3175	3222	8 16 24	31 39
53	1·3270	3319	3367	3416	3465	3514	3564	3613	3663	3713	8 16 25	33 41
54	1·3764	3814	3865	3916	3968	4019	4071	4124	4176	4229	9 17 26	34 43
55	1·4281	4335	4388	4442	4496	4550	4605	4659	4715	4770	9 18 27	36 45
56	1·4826	4882	4938	4994	5051	5108	5166	5224	5282	5310	10 19 29	38 48
57	1·5399	5458	5517	5577	5637	5697	5757	5818	5880	5941	10 20 30	40 50
58	1·6003	6066	6128	6191	6255	6319	6383	6447	6512	6577	11 21 32	43 53
59	1·6643	6709	6775	6842	6909	6977	7045	7113	7182	7251	11 23 34	45 56
60	1·7321	7391	7461	7532	7603	7675	7747	7820	7893	7966	12 24 36	48 60
61	1·8040	8115	8190	8265	8341	8418	8495	8572	8650	8728	13 26 38	51 64
62	1·8807	8887	8967	9047	9128	9210	9292	9375	9458	9542	14 27 41	55 68
63	1·9626	9711	9797	9883	9970	2·0057	2·0145	2·0233	2·0323	2·0413	15 29 44	58 73
64	2·0503	0594	0686	0778	0872	0965	1060	1155	1251	1348	16 31 47	63 78
65	2·1445	1543	1642	1742	1842	1943	2045	2148	2251	2355	17 34 51	68 85
66	2·2460	2566	2673	2781	2889	2998	3109	3220	3332	3445	18 37 55	73 92
67	2·3559	3673	3789	3906	4023	4142	4262	4383	4504	4627	20 40 60	79 99
68	2·4751	4876	5002	5129	5257	5386	5517	5649	5782	5916	22 43 65	87 108
69	2·6051	6187	6325	6464	6605	6746	6889	7034	7179	7326	24 47 71	95 119
70	2·7475	7625	7776	7929	8083	8239	8397	8556	8716	8878	26 52 78	104 131
71	2·9042	9208	9375	9544	9714	9887	3·0061	3·0237	3·0415	3·0595	29 58 87	116 145
72	3·0777	0961	1146	1334	1524	1716	1910	2106	2305	2506	32 64 96	129 161
73	3·2709	2914	3122	3332	3544	3759	3977	4197	4420	4646	36 72 108	144 180
74	3·4874	5105	5339	5576	5816	6059	6305	6554	6806	7062	41 81 122	163 204
75	3·7321	7583	7848	8118	8391	8667	8947	9232	9520	9812	46 93 139	186 232
76	4·0108	0408	0713	1022	1335	1653	1976	2303	2635	2972	53 107 160	213 267
77	4·3315	3662	4015	4374	4737	5107	5483	5864	6252	6646		
78	4·7046	7453	7867	8288	8716	9152	9594	5·0045	5·0504	5·0970	Mean differences cease	
79	5·1446	1929	2422	2924	3435	3955	4486	5026	5578	6140	to be sufficiently accurate.	
80	5·6713	7297	7894	8502	9124	9758	6·0405	6·1066	6·1742	6·2432		
81	6·3138	3859	4596	5350	6122	6912	7720	8548	9395	7·0264		
82	7·1154	2066	3002	3962	4947	5958	6996	8062	9158	8·0285		
83	8·1443	2636	3863	5126	6427	7769	9152	9·0579	9·2052	9·3572		
84	9·5144	9·677	9·845	10·02	10·20	10·39	10·58	10·78	10·99	11·20		
85	11·43	11·66	11·91	12·16	12·43	12·71	13·00	13·30	13·62	13·95		
86	14·30	14·67	15·00	15·16	15·89	16·35	16·83	17·34	17·89	18·46		
87	19·08	19·74	20·45	21·20	22·02	22·90	23·86	24·90	26·03	27·27		
88	28·64	30·14	31·82	33·69	35·80	38·19	40·92	44·07	47·74	52·08		
89	57·29	63·66	71·62	81·85	95·49	114·6	143·2	191·0	286·5	573·0		
90	∞											

Answers to questions

1) a) 364. b) 9720. c) 19750. d) 220639 e) 9022345.

2)

27	63	30	2	28
65	27	28	27	3
30	26	35	26	33
7	25	26	28	64
21	9	31	67	22

3)

39	50	40	13	38
52	38	38	38	14
39	37	36	35	33
17	34	34	34	61
33	21	32	60	34

4) a) 644. b) 68302. c) 6908528. d) 690860280. e) 69094714535.

5) 310 seats, £3928.

6) a) 77. b) 134. c) 2272. d) 47188. e) 1521.

7) 16 miles.

8) a) 421. b) 662. c) 435. d) 542. e) 638.

9) 4.

10) 6769.

11) The total value of the five kinds of coin = $\frac{79.98}{93}$ = 86p. The value of each coin
= 50p, 20p, 10p, 5p and 1p.

12) 3.

13) a) 0.20, 20%. b) $\frac{1}{4}$, 25%. c) $\frac{2}{5}$, 0.40.

14) 45.

15) a) $\frac{62}{63}$. b) $\frac{35}{36}$.

16) 115°.

17) 112 miles.

18) See diagram overleaf

Triangles ABC and ADE are similar, $\frac{0.7}{18} = \frac{X}{126}$

Cross multiplying, $18X = 0.7 \times 126$, $X = \frac{0.7 \times 126}{18} = 4.9$ m

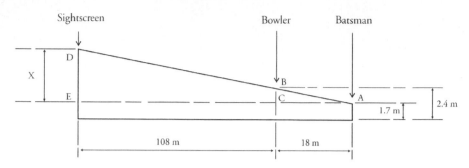

Sightscreen   Bowler   Batsman

Required height of sightscreen = 4.9 + 1.7 = <u>6.6m or 21.7ft.</u>

19) AB = 12, AC = 7.21.

20) H = 4.

21)

    a) BC = 6, Angle A = 36° 52′, Angle C = 53° 8′.

    b) BC = 6.16, Angle B = 46° 55′.

    c) Angle A = 39° 24′, Angle B = 54° 42′, Angle C = 85° 54′.

22) 7.85 m.

23) Arc AB = 4.71, Chord AB = 4.24.

24) Radius = 7.5.

25) If the distance the captain can see ahead is D (metres):

$$(6375 \times 1000)^2 + D^2 = (6375 \times 1000 + 10)^2$$

$$\cancel{(6375 \times 1000)^2} + D^2 = \cancel{(6375 \times 1000)^2} + 20000 \times 6375 + 100.$$

Since 100 is very small compared
to 20000×6375

$$D = \sqrt{20000 \times 6375}$$

$$= \sqrt{127.5 \times 10^3}$$

$$= \underline{11,292 \text{ metres} = 7 \text{ miles}}$$

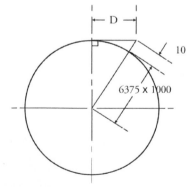

26) a) 2.83 m, b) 5m.

27) a) AC = 3m, since triangle ACD has 3 equal sides.

$$BD = \sqrt{(3(1 + \cos60°))^2 + (3\sin60°)^2}$$

$$= \sqrt{(3(1 + 0.5))^2 + (3 \times 0.866)^2}$$

$$= \sqrt{4.5^2 + 2.598^2}$$

$$= \sqrt{20.25 + 6.75}$$

$$= \sqrt{27} = \underline{5.20 \text{ m}}$$

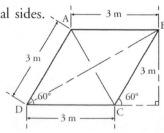

b)

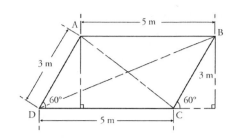

$$AC = \sqrt{(5 - 3\cos60°)^2 + (3\sin60°)^2}$$
$$= \sqrt{(5 - 1.5)^2 + (3 \times 0.866)^2}$$
$$= \sqrt{3.5^2 + 2.598^2}$$
$$= \sqrt{12.25 + 6.75}$$
$$= \sqrt{19} = \underline{4.36 \text{ m}}$$
$$BD = \sqrt{(5 + 3\cos60°)^2 + (3\sin60°)^2}$$
$$= \sqrt{(1 + 1.5)^2 + (3 \times 0.866)^2}$$
$$= \sqrt{6.5^2 + 2.598^2}$$
$$= \sqrt{42.25 + 6.75}$$
$$= \sqrt{49} = \underline{7 \text{ m}}$$

28) a)

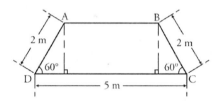

$$AB = 5 - 2 \times 2\cos60°$$
$$= 5 - 2 = \underline{3 \text{ m}}$$

b)

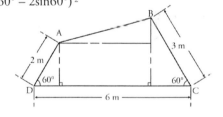

$$AB = \sqrt{(6 - 3\cos60° - 2\cos60°)^2 + (3\sin60° - 2\sin60°)^2}$$
$$= \sqrt{(6 - 5 \times 0.5)^2 + (0.866)^2}$$
$$= \sqrt{3.5^2 + 0.866^2}$$
$$= \sqrt{12.25 + 0.75}$$
$$= \sqrt{13} = \underline{3.61 \text{ m}}$$

29) a) 20. b) 21. c) 31.5.

30) a) 9 m². b) 10 m². c) 15 m². d) 15 m².

31) Area of rectangle = 0.98 m²
Area of 4 triangles = 0.49 m²
Area of rhombus = 0.98 m² – 0.49 m² = <u>0.49 m²</u>

32) Area of Triangle OAB = 0.5R × 0.866R = 0.433R² = <u>0.97 m²</u>

Area of segment OAB = $\dfrac{\pi R^2}{6}$ = 0.52R² = <u>1.18 m²</u>.

33) Area of walls and ceiling = (2 × 3 × 6) + (2 × 3 × 8) + (6 × 8)
$$= 36 + 48 + 48 = \underline{132 \text{ m}^2}$$

Paint required = $\dfrac{132}{15}$ = 8.8, say <u>9 litres.</u>

Carpet required = 6 × 8 = <u>48m².</u>

34) a)1898.4 cm³. b) 523598.7 cm³ c) 37699.1 cm³. d) 1134.1 cm³.

35) Kitchen air volume = $4 \times 3 \times 2.5 = 30 m^3$.

For 15 air changes per hour, Fan size = $15 \times 30 = \underline{450 m^3/hr}$.

36) Volume of pool = $1 \times 15 \times 20 + 2 \times 25 \times 20 = 300 + 1000 = \underline{1300 m^3}$.

37) Volume of container = $5 \times 10^6 mm^3$.

$$\text{Volume of funnel} = \frac{1}{3} \pi \times 62.5^2 \times 125 - \frac{1}{3} \pi \times 5^2 \times 10$$

$$= 511327 - 262 = 511075 \ mm^3$$

$$\text{Number of fillings} = \frac{5000000}{511075} = 9.8 \ \text{say} \ \underline{10}.$$

38) Volume of shaving cream in tube = $\frac{\pi}{4} \times 3^2 \times 13.5 = 95.43 \ cm^3$.

Volume/shave $= \frac{\pi}{4} \times 0.75^2 \times 2.7 = 1.19 \ cm^3$

Number of shaves $= \dfrac{95.43}{1.19} = \underline{80}.$

39) Volume of glass $= \frac{\pi}{4}(2.625^2 - 2.5^2) \ 3 + \frac{\pi}{4} \times 2.625^2 \times 0.25$

$$= \frac{\pi}{4}(6.891 - 6.250) \ 3 + \frac{\pi}{4} \times 6.891 \times 0.25$$

$$= \frac{\pi}{4}(1.923 + 1.723)$$

$$= \frac{\pi}{4} \ 3.646 = \underline{2.864 in^3}.$$

Volume of water $= \frac{\pi}{4} \times 2.5^2 \times 3 = \underline{14.726 \ in^3}$

Weight of tumbler empty $= 2.864 \times 0.095 \ = 0.27$ lbs. ⎫
Weight of water $= 14.726 \times 0.036 = 0.53$ lbs. ⎬
Weight of tumble full of water $= \underline{0.80}$ lbs. ⎭

40) Volume of steel = $(4 \times 4 - \frac{\pi}{4} \times 2.5^2) \ 2$

$$= (16 - 4.91) \ 2 = \underline{22.18 \ in^3}.$$

Volume of bush $= \frac{\pi}{4}(2.5^2 - 2^2) \ 2.$

$$= \frac{\pi}{2} \times 2.5 = \underline{3.53 \ in^3}.$$

Weight of steel $= 22.18 \times 0.282 = 6.25$ lbs. ⎫
Weight of brass $= 3.53 \times 0.309 \ = 1.09$ lbs ⎪
Weight of nylon $= 3.53 \times 0.045 \ = 0.16$ lbs. ⎬
Weight of housing and brass bush $= 22.18 \times 0.282 = 7.34$ lbs. ⎪
Reduction in weight $= \underline{0.93}$ lbs. ⎭

41) Volume of mercury $= \dfrac{\pi}{4} (5^2 \times 15 + 0.5^2 \times 100)$

$\qquad\qquad\qquad\quad = \dfrac{\pi}{4} (25 \times 15 + 0.25 \times 100)$

$\qquad\qquad\qquad\quad = \dfrac{\pi}{4} (375 + 25)$

$\qquad\qquad\qquad\quad = \dfrac{\pi}{4} 400 = 314 \text{ mm}^2 = \underline{0.314 \text{ cc.}}$

$\quad$ Volume of Glass $= \dfrac{\pi}{4} (7^2 \times 300 - 5^2 \times 15 - 0.5^2 \times 283)$

$\qquad\qquad\qquad\quad = \dfrac{\pi}{4} (49 \times 300 - 375 - 70.75)$

$\qquad\qquad\qquad\quad = \dfrac{\pi}{4} (14700 - 445.75)$

$\qquad\qquad\qquad\quad = \dfrac{\pi}{4} 14254.25 = 11195 \text{ mm}^3 = \underline{11.195 \text{ cc.}}$

$\quad$ Weight of Mercury $= 0.314 \times 13.55 = 4.25$ grams.
$\quad$ Weight of Glass $\quad = 11.195 \times 2.63 = 29.44$ grams.
$\quad$ Total Weight $\qquad\qquad\qquad\qquad = \underline{33.69 \text{ grams.}}$

42) Volume of wood top $= 800 \times 800 \times 15 = 9600000 \text{ mm}^3$.
$\quad$ Volume of plastic top $= 800 \times 800 \times 3 = 1920000 \text{ mm}^3$.

$\quad$ Volume of legs $\quad = 4 \times \dfrac{\pi}{4} \times 25^2 \times 700 = 1374447 \text{ mm}^3$.

$\quad$ Weight of wood top $\qquad = 9600 \times 0.47 = 4512$ grams.
$\quad$ Weight of plastic top $\quad = 1920 \times 0.94 = 1805$ grams.
$\quad$ Weight of legs $\qquad\quad = 1374 \times 0.86 = 1182$ grams
$\quad$ Total weight $\qquad\qquad\qquad\qquad = 7499$ grams $= \underline{7.5 \text{ kilograms.}}$

43) Distance travelled $- 1 + 0.1 = 1.1$ miles at 30 mph.

$\quad$ Time taken $= \dfrac{1.1}{30} \times 60 = 2.2$ minutes $= \underline{2 \text{ mins } 12 \text{ secs.}}$

44) Volume of half-full bath $= 1.5 \times 0.6 \times 0.2 = 0.18\text{m}^3$

$\quad$ time taken $= \dfrac{0.18}{0.02} = \underline{9\text{mins.}}$

45) Deceleration $= \dfrac{88 - 44}{10} = \dfrac{44}{10} = \underline{4.4\text{ft/sec/sec.}}$

46) Number of cars $= \dfrac{44}{4} = 10$

$\quad$ 70 mph $= 102.7$ ft/sec, so gap between cars $= 2 \times 102.7 = 205.4$ft.
$\quad$ Space occupied by cars $= 10$ car lengths $+ 9$ gaps between cars.
$\qquad\qquad\qquad\qquad = 10 \times 15 + 9 \times 205.4$
$\qquad\qquad\qquad\qquad = 150 + 1848.6 = \underline{1999 \text{ ft.}}$

Ratio : $\dfrac{\text{Space occupied by cars}}{\text{Space occupied by bus}} = \dfrac{1999}{45} = \dfrac{44.4}{1}$

47) The car travels 135ft at 44ft/sec, so the time taken $= \dfrac{135}{44} = 3.1$ secs.

The relative speed between car and moving vehicle $= 60 - 55$

$= 5$ mph $= 7.33$ ft/sec.

Time taken $= \dfrac{135}{7.33} = 18.4$ secs.

Distance travelled by car $= 88 \times 18.4 = 1619$ft $= 0.3$ miles.

48) Roads = 40%.
Schools = 25.7%.
Social and other services = 8.6% each.
Fire Service = 5.7%.
Waste Disposal and Police = 4.3% each.
Libraries = 2.8%.

49) Average Salary = £22000.

50) Average diameter of roll $= \dfrac{12 + 5}{2} = 8.5$cm.

Number of thicknesses of paper on roll $= \dfrac{\text{Outside radius} - \text{Inside radius}}{\text{paper thickness}}$

$= \dfrac{60 - 25}{0.125} = 280.$

Length of paper on roll $= \pi \times$ Average diameter $\times$ number of thicknesses.

$= \pi \times 8.5 \times 280 = 7477$ cm $= 74.77$ metres.

Index